Songs on favourite themes

Su Garnett

Credits

Author
Su Garnett

Editor
Jane Bishop

Assistant Editor
Jennifer Shiels

Series Designer
Anna Oliwa

Designer
Geraldine Reidy

Cover Illustration
Chris Simpson

Illustrations
Louise Gardner

Music setting
Sally Scott

All songs supplied by CYP.

Designed using Adobe InDesign

Published by Scholastic Ltd
Villiers House
Clarendon Avenue
Leamington Spa
Warwickshire
CV32 5PR

www.scholastic.co.uk

Printed by Bell & Bain

2 3 4 5 6 7 8 9   5 6 7 8 9 0 1 2 3 4

British Library Cataloguing-in-Publication Data
A catalogue record for this book is available from the British Library.

ISBN 0-439-97172-1
ISBN 9-780-439-97172-0

Acknowledgement

Qualifications and Curriculum Authority for the use of extracts from the QCA/DfEE document *Curriculum Guidance for the Foundation Stage* © 2000 Qualifications and Curriculum Authority.

Every effort has been made to trace copyright holders for the works reproduced in this book, and the publishers apologise for any inadvertent omissions.

Contents

Contents

Growing

Transport

People who help us

Introduction

Using songs for learning

Children have always loved songs and they enjoy joining in with music that they know well. With repeated playing, new songs are easily absorbed and learning takes place effortlessly and enjoyably. This is the value of songs for learning – the children learn without even realising that they are being taught something new. The aim of this book is to provide practitioners with a useful bank of songs to use with children, in order to promote and encourage their learning in all six areas of the curriculum.

Regular use of well-known and well-loved songs and rhymes, helps to build the children's confidence and invites them to take part in a shared activity. This encourages the children to be involved with the group as a whole, and makes learning accessible and easy.

Songs instil a love of music and rhythm, and also encourage an awareness of rhyme, all of which are important learning skills. Overall, the book will make theme-based learning even more meaningful and enjoyable for children.

How to use this book

For each song on the CD, there are four pages in the book. The first spread provides the musical score on the left-hand page, and the words and suggested actions on the right-hand page. The second double-page spread has ideas for how to use the song and follow-up activities on the left-hand page, and an accompanying photocopiable on the right-hand page (except for the last song, which does not have an accompanying photocopiable).

'Sharing the song' explains the learning concepts that can be developed through the song with suggested themes, as well as appropriate times for singing the song and ideas for introducing it.

'Activity ideas' suggests activities to follow up the song's concepts and themes. Each song is linked to a Stepping Stone and an Early Learning Goal. Collectively, the activity ideas cover all six Areas of Learning in the QCA document *Curriculum Guidance for the Foundation Stage*. See box, below, for shorthand used.

Start by listening to the songs on the CD as a group and explain the meaning of any new words to the children. Use the accompanying activity ideas to develop and extend the children's learning within a certain theme.

How to make the most of the songs

Use the songs regularly so that the children become totally familiar with them and can really enjoy singing the words.

Encourage the children to join in with the actions and to engage in role-play, using the props and costumes as outlined in the activity ideas.

To develop the children's speech and understanding, introduce each of the songs with questions directed at the group and encourage general discussion. Use the accompanying photocopiable sheets to consolidate the children's learning from the activities.

Areas of Learning

PSED Personal, social and emotional education
CLL Communication, language and literacy
MD Mathematical development
KUW Knowledge and understanding of the world
PD Physical development
CD Creative development

Myself

Head, Shoulders, Knees and Toes

Head, Shoulders, Knees and Toes

(Children stand and point, with both hands, to the parts of the body throughout the song.)

Head, shoulders, knees and toes,
Knees and toes.
Head, shoulders, knees and toes,
Knees and toes.
And eyes and ears and mouth and nose,
Head, shoulders, knees and toes.

(Repeat)

Cheeks and chin, knees and toes,
Knees and toes.
Cheeks and chin, knees and toes,
Knees and toes.
And eyes and ears and mouth and nose,
Cheeks and chin, knees and toes.

Head, shoulders, knees and toes,
Knees and toes.
Head, shoulders, knees and toes,
Knees and toes.
And eyes and ears and mouth and nose,
Head, shoulders, knees and toes.

Arms and elbows, knees and toes,
Knees and toes.
Arms and elbows, knees and toes,
Knees and toes.
And eyes and ears and mouth and nose,
Arms and elbows, knees and toes.

Head, shoulders, knees and toes,
Knees and toes.
Head, shoulders, knees and toes,
Knees and toes.
And eyes and ears and mouth and nose,
Head, shoulders, knees and toes.

(Repeat)

Head, Shoulders, Knees and Toes

How to use this song

Learning objectives

Stepping Stone
Combine and repeat a range of movements.

Early Learning Goal
Move with control and coordination. **(PD)**

Group size
Any size.

Props
Shorts and T-shirts, or leotards.

Sharing the song

This song can be linked to the themes of 'Myself' or 'My body'.

Ask the group to put on their shorts and T-shirts, or leotards, ready to perform the song.

The children will enjoy bending and stretching their bodies as they join in with this song. Start by singing the song quite slowly to give them plenty of time to point to the various parts of their bodies, in the correct order. As they become more competent and faster at remembering the order of movements, you can ask them to sing the song at a quicker speed, thus increasing their control over their bodies.

Use this song as part of a warm-up session for a spell of physical activity. Stress the importance of keeping our bodies fit and healthy, and of exercising muscles in order to keep them strong and supple. Talk about different forms of exercise, such as riding bicycles, swimming, running and so on.

Activity ideas

- Encourage the children to do some simple counting exercises, by counting the number of parts of the body mentioned in the first line of the song, and then those mentioned in the fifth line. How many is that altogether? (Emphasise that four and four makes eight altogether). Note the answers for adding other pairs together, for example, one and one makes two (count eyes, ears, hands and feet); two and two makes four; three and three makes six (count fingers and toes). **(MD)**

- Encourage an understanding of sequence and order by making copies of the photocopiable sheet, and asking the children to follow the sequence by drawing a line across the page to the body part that comes next in the song. **(MD)**

- Invite the children to explore how their knees can move. Ask them to stretch right up and bend right down, curling into a ball, before kneeling down on the floor. Next, ask them to sit down on the floor and cross their legs, before stretching out their legs and pointing their toes. Encourage them to be aware of their knees as they do so. Explain that none of these movements would be possible without flexible knee joints. **(PD)**

- Draw a large egg shape on to card. Ask the children to finish off the head by adding hair and drawing in a face with eyes, nose, mouth and ears. Encourage them to put in as much detail as possible. Invite the children to tell you if their drawing is of someone they know, or if it is an imaginary face. **(CD)**

Head, Shoulders, Knees and Toes

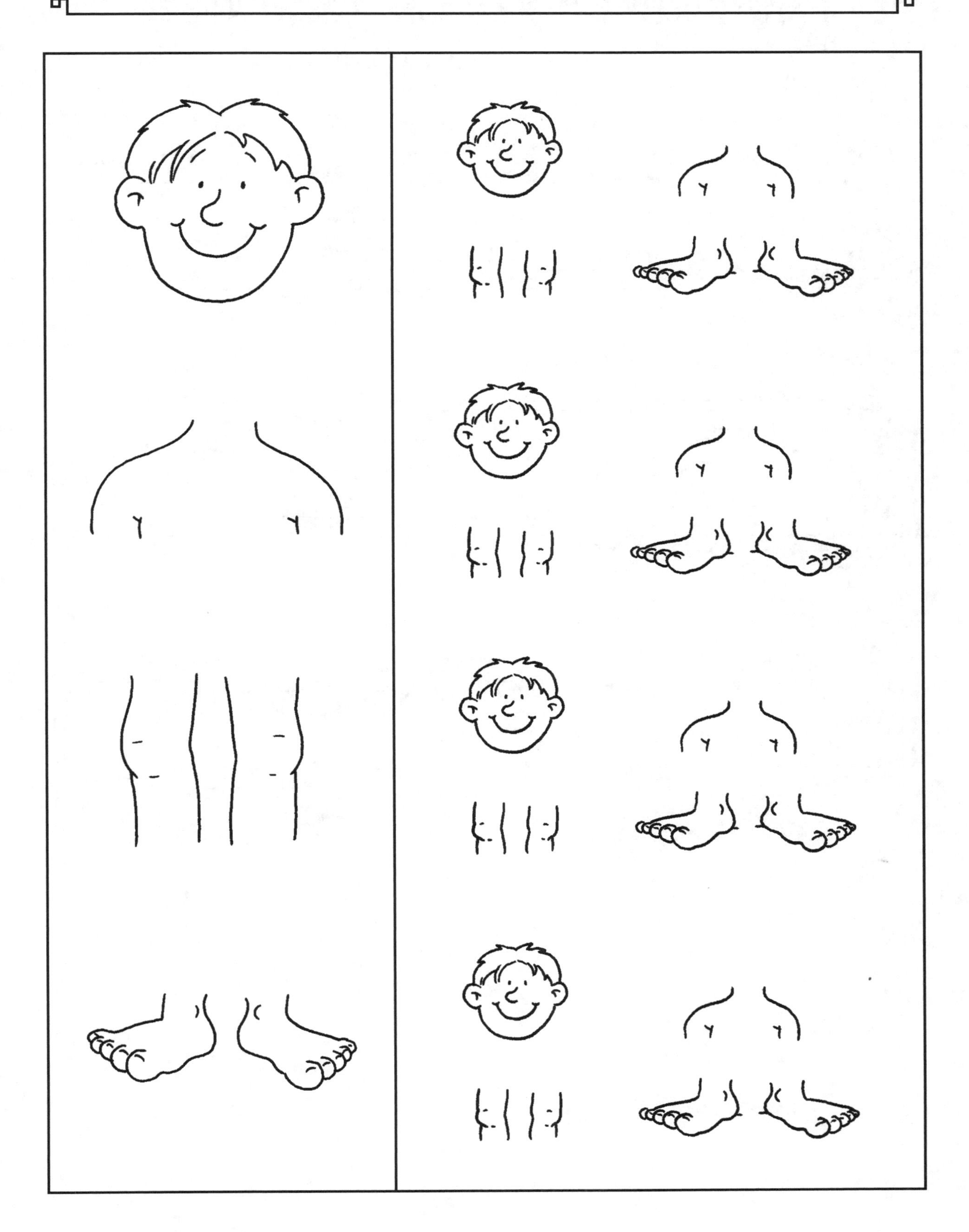

Put Your Finger on Your Nose

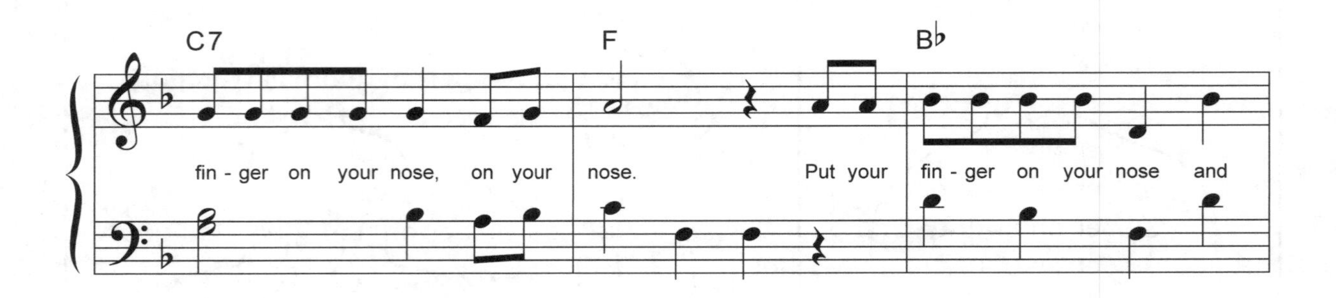

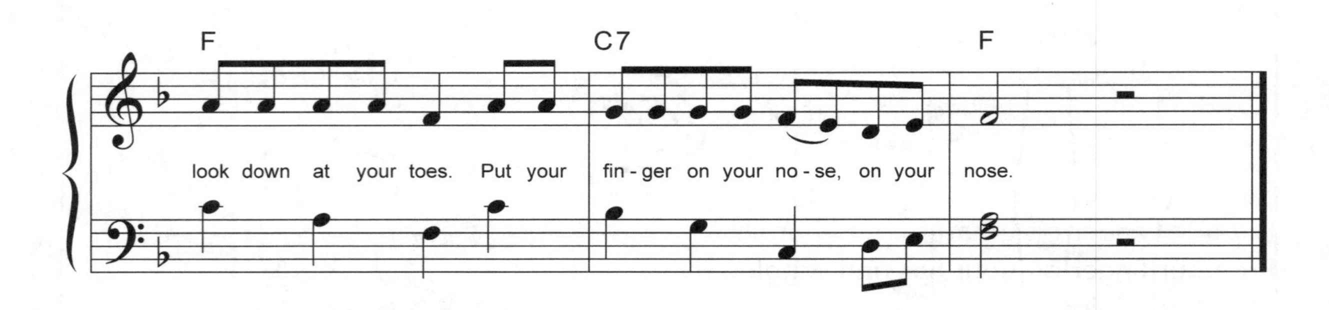

Put Your Finger on Your Nose

(Place index finger on nose.)
Put your finger on your nose, on your nose.
Put your finger on your nose, on your nose.
Put your finger on your nose and look down at your toes.
(Look down to toes.)

Put your finger on your nose, on your nose.
(Place index finger on nose.)

(Place index finger on ear.)
Put your finger on your ear, on your ear.
Put your finger on your ear, on your ear.
Put your finger on your ear, now what can you hear?
(Cup hand around ear.)

Put your finger on your ear, on your ear.
(Place index finger on ear.)

(Place index finger on lips.)
Put your finger on your lips, on your lips.
Put your finger on your lips, on your lips.
Put your finger on your lips and wiggle round your hips.
(Wiggle hips.)

Put your finger on your lips, on your lips.
(Place index finger on lips.)

(Place index finger on knee.)
Put your finger on your knee, on your knee.
Put your finger on your knee, on your knee.
Put your finger on your knee and dance along with me.
(Skip around.)

Put your finger on your knee, on your knee.
(Place index finger on knee.)

(Place index finger on chin.)
Put your finger on your chin, on your chin.
Put your finger on your chin, on your chin.
Put your finger on your chin and give a cheeky grin.
(Give a big smile.)

Put your finger on your chin, on your chin.
(Place index finger on chin.)

(Place index finger on other hand.)
Put your finger on your hand, on your hand.
Put your finger on your hand, on your hand.
Put your finger on your hand and listen to the band.
(Pretend to conduct a band.)

Put your finger on your hand, on your hand.
(Place index finger on other hand.)

(Place index finger on nose.)
Put your finger on your nose, on your nose.
Put your finger on your nose, on your nose.
Put your finger on your nose and look down at your toes.
(Look down to toes.)

Put your finger on your nose, on your nose.
(Place index finger on nose.)

Put Your Finger on Your Nose

How to use this song

Learning objectives

Stepping Stone
Respond to simple instructions.

Early Learning Goal
Sustain attentive listening, responding to what they have heard by relevant actions. **(CLL)**

Group size
Any size.

Props
Musical instruments, such as a drum, triangle and tambourine.

Sharing the song

The song is particularly relevant to the themes of 'Myself' and 'Senses'.

Suggest that the children each have an instrument to play when they 'listen to the band' in the song.

The aim of this song is to encourage the children to listen carefully and to follow simple instructions. The addition of actions makes the whole process much more fun and introduces a sense of purpose to the learning process. The message is, if you do not listen, you cannot join in successfully and do what everyone else is doing.

Introduce this song at a time when the children are still alert and ready to listen carefully. It could be used as a practice for listening carefully when you are about to give the children important instructions, for example, prior to a trip.

When you introduce the song, talk about why we need to follow instructions quickly and carefully. You could sensitively approach the need to respond to a serious situation by doing exactly as the practitioner says.

Activity ideas

- Encourage the children to listen very carefully and to notice rhyming words in the song. Start by reading any simple texts that introduce rhyming words and point these out to the children. When they are quite competent at noticing the words that rhyme, hesitate as you come to the rhyme, so that the children can anticipate the word that is coming next. Make copies of the photocopiable sheet and invite the children to find the rhyming words, drawing a line to the pictures that match. **(CLL)**

- Play games involving following the leader, to encourage the children to watch carefully and copy actions. Practise dancing in time to different types of music and in response to the leader's actions. Let the children take it in turns to be the leader and to choose the movements that they want to make. **(PD)**

- Talk about the senses and the jobs that different parts of the body do. Concentrate on the senses mentioned in the song, for example, the ear for hearing and the nose for smelling. Sing the song in various areas, noticing what you hear and smell in each, such as aeroplanes and cut grass outside, shutting doors and food being cooked inside. Encourage the children to sit quietly to really appreciate the sounds around them. **(CD)**

Put Your Finger on Your Nose

Dem Bones

F
C
Dem bones, dem bones, dem dry bones. Dem bones, dem bones, dem
F
C7
dry bones. Dem bones, dem bones, dem dry bones. Now hear the word of the
F
F
Lord. The toe bone's con - nec - ted to the foot bone. The
C
F
foot bone's con - nec - ted to the ank - le bone. The ank - le bone's con - nec - ted to the
C7
F
leg bone. Now hear the word of the Lord.

Dem Bones

Dem bones, dem bones, dem dry bones.
Dem bones, dem bones, dem dry bones.
Dem bones, dem bones, dem dry bones.
Now hear the word of the Lord.

(Sit on the floor, with legs outstretched and point to the bone joints in turn.)
The toe bone's connected to the foot bone.
The foot bone's connected to the ankle bone.
The ankle bone's connected to the leg bone.
Now hear the word of the Lord.

The leg bone's connected to the thigh bone.
The thigh bone's connected to the hip bone.
The hip bone's connected to the back bone.
Now hear the word of the Lord.

The back bone's connected to the shoulder bone.
The shoulder bone's connected to the neck bone.
The neck bone's connected to the head bone.
Now hear the word of the Lord.

Dem bones, dem bones gonna walk around.
Dem bones, dem bones gonna walk around.
Dem bones, dem bones gonna walk around.
Now hear the word of the Lord.

Dem Bones

How to use this song

Learning objectives

Stepping Stone
Talk about what is seen and what is happening.

Early Learning Goal
Ask questions about why things happen and how things work. **(KUW)**

Group size
Any size.

Props
Model skeleton or X-ray pictures (optional).

Sharing the song

The purpose of this song is to make the children aware of the bones in their bodies and how the way that these bones are joined together helps them to move around in all the different ways that they can. The song links well with the themes of 'Myself' and 'People who help us'. It could be sung as part of circle time or as a cooling-off activity before the children go home.

Discuss going to the doctor and whether any of the children have ever broken any bones, or had X-rays to see whether they might have done. Explain how a plaster cast keeps the broken bone very still while it mends itself. If possible, show the children a life-size model skeleton or X-ray pictures, so that they can clearly see how the various bones in the body join together. As an alternative or as reinforcement, use the skeleton on the photocopiable sheet. Use a computer to print out the words 'toe', 'foot', 'ankle', 'leg', 'thigh', 'hip', 'back', 'shoulder', 'neck' and 'head'. Let the children cut these out and label an enlarged copy of the skeleton.

Activity ideas

- Invite the children to look carefully at their hands and arms. Help them to count the number of joints between the tips of the fingers and their shoulder. Notice the two joints in the fingers before the knuckles, the wrist joint, the elbow and finally the shoulder. Point out that each finger has two joints before it joins on to the rest of the hand at the knuckles. Encourage the children to count up in twos, until they reach the total number of joints for each hand. **(MD)**

- Show the children the effect of oil on a tool that has moving parts (for example, scissors or pliers), which have seized up. Explain the need for us to lubricate our bodies in the same way, so that our joints continue to work properly. Tell them that the oil we need is present in the food we eat. **(KUW)**

- Help the children to cut out small rectangles (approximately 10cm×3cm) of different-coloured card to resemble bones. Help them to punch a small hole in one end of each card. Put two pieces of card together and let the children feed in a brass-headed paper fastener, folding back the arms underneath the card. Let the children experiment with the joined cards and see how the two pieces move smoothly and independently from each other. Make the comparison with bone joints. **(CD)**

Dem Bones

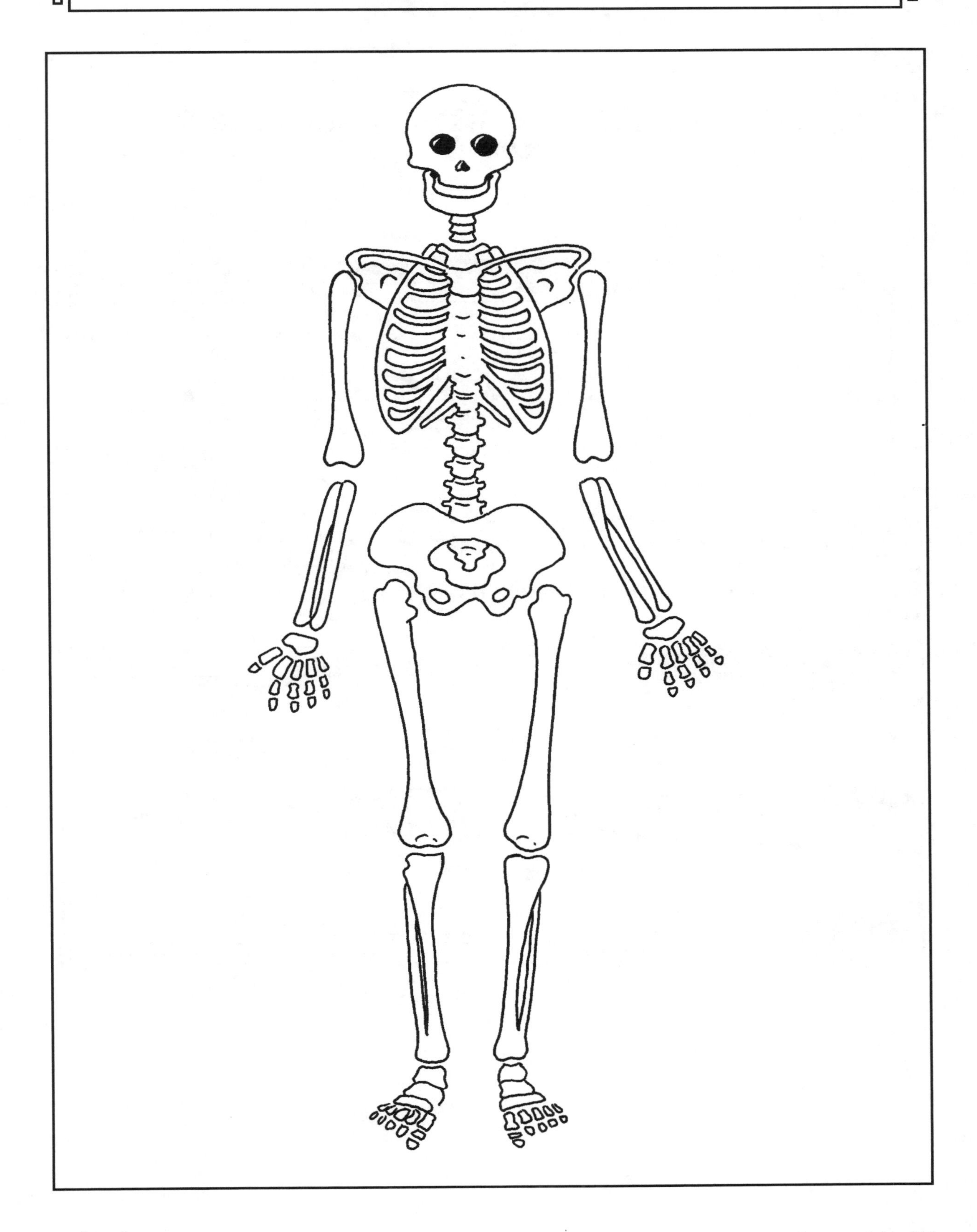

My day

If You're Happy and You Know It

If You're Happy and You Know It

(Stand up or sit down, follow the instructions and carry out the actions.)

If you're happy and you know it,
Clap your hands.
If you're happy and you know it,
Clap your hands.
If you're happy and you know it,
And you really want to show it,
If you're happy and you know it,
Clap your hands.

If you're happy and you know it,
Stamp your feet.
If you're happy and you know it,
Stamp your feet.
If you're happy and you know it,
And you really want to show it,
If you're happy and you know it,
Stamp your feet.

If you're happy and you know it,
Nod your head.
If you're happy and you know it,
Nod your head.
If you're happy and you know it,
And you really want to show it,
If you're happy and you know it,
Nod your head.

If you're happy and you know it,
Do all three.
If you're happy and you know it,
Do all three.
If you're happy and you know it,
And you really want to show it,
If you're happy and you know it,
Do all three.

If you're happy and you know it,
Shout 'hoorah'.
If you're happy and you know it,
Shout 'hoorah'.
If you're happy and you know it,
And you really want to show it,
If you're happy and you know it,
Shout 'hoorah'.

If You're Happy and You Know It

How to use this song

Learning objectives

Stepping Stone
Express needs and feelings in appropriate ways.

Early Learning Goal
Respond to significant experiences, showing a range of feelings when appropriate. **(PSED)**

Group size
Any size.

Props
Paper-plate smiley faces (see below).

Sharing the song

This is a happy song where everyone can express their joy by joining in enthusiastically with the actions of the song. The aim of the song is to help the children to express their feelings openly, to share them with others and not to bottle them up. The song links in very well with the themes of 'Myself', or 'My day'.

Invite each child to make a smiley face by drawing a face on to a paper plate and attaching a circle of masking tape to the back. Suggest that the children wear their smiley faces on their chests, by sticking them on to their clothes with the masking tape.

Use this song as part of circle time, to encourage the children to share their feelings, whether they are positive or negative, with the group. Alter the song and the corresponding actions to match the children's moods, for example, 'If you're angry and you know it, growl out loud'.

Talk about the different feelings that people have at different times, as a result of things that are happening to them. Explain how most people have lots of energy when they are feeling happy and quite often want to move around, do things and share their happiness with other people.

Activity ideas

- Encourage the children to talk about what makes them happy, sad, frustrated, angry, frightened, excited and so on. What seems fair and unfair? Reinforce the discussion by using the photocopiable sheet. Make a copy for each child and encourage them to match up the pictures of the various scenes with the expressive faces, to show how the characters might be feeling in the different situations. **(PSED)**

- Introduce positional language by asking the children to clap their hands low down, high up, in front of their bodies, behind their bodies, between their legs and so on. Can they clap their hands or stamp their feet a certain number of times? Invite them to copy patterns by clapping out rhythms that you introduce on a tambourine, such as slow, quick, quick, slow. **(MD)**

- Ask the children to create a picture, collage or model using colours and items that make them feel happy. These might include bright reds and yellows, furry material, shiny sequins, sunshine, stars, flowers, animals and so on. Can the children explain to the rest of the group why these particular things make them feel happy? Do they have particular associations with these things? **(CD)**

If You're Happy and You Know It

I Went to School One Morning

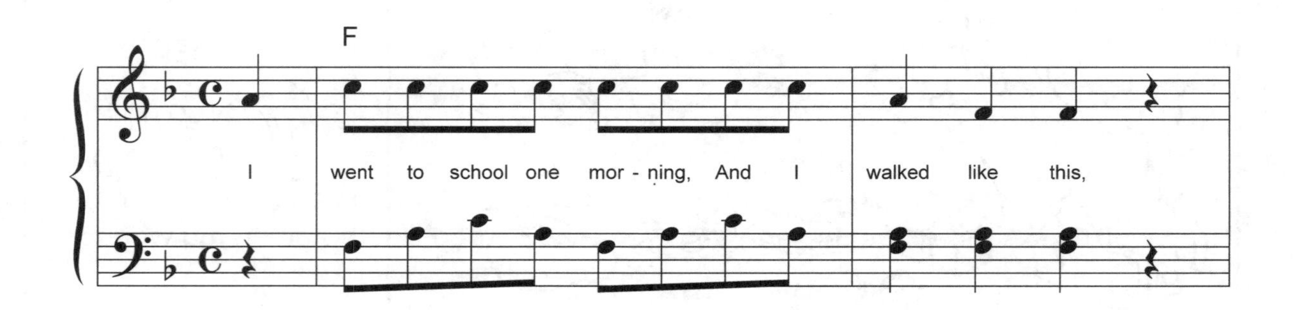

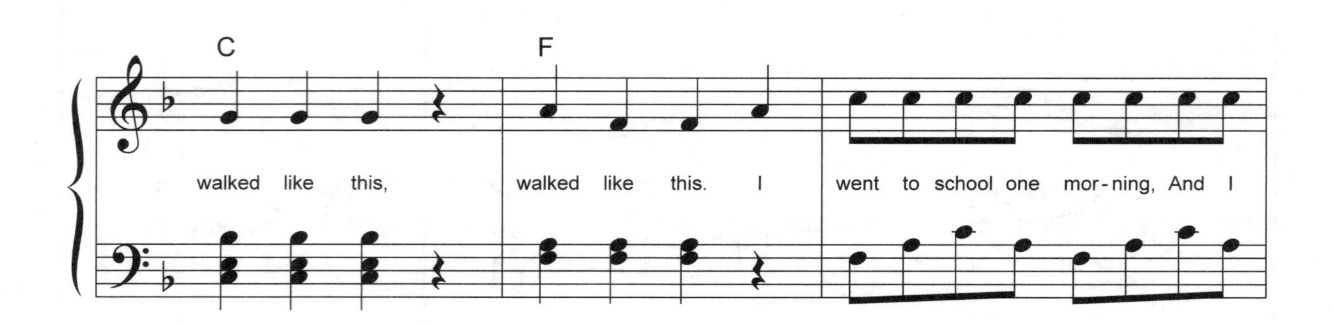

I Went to School One Morning

I went to school one morning,
And I walked like this, walked like this, walked like this.
(Walk quickly in pairs, holding hands with partner.)

I went to school one morning,
And I walked like this all on my way to school.

I saw a little robin,
And I hopped like this, hopped like this, hopped like this.
(Hop along.)

I saw a little robin,
And I hopped like this all on my way to school.

I saw a shiny river,
And I splashed like this, splashed like this, splashed like this.
(Pretend to be splashing through a puddle, lifting feet high and putting them down hard.)

I saw a shiny river,
And I splashed like this all on my way to school.

I saw a little pony,
And I galloped like this, galloped like this, galloped like this.
(Skip along, raising knees high off the ground.)

I saw a little pony,
And I galloped like this all on my way to school.

I saw a tall policeman,
And I stood like this, stood like this, stood like this.
(Stand up tall, feet together, head held high.)

I saw a tall policeman,
And I stood like this all on my way to school.

I heard the school bell ringing,
And I ran like this, ran like this, ran like this.
(Run quickly.)

I heard the school bell ringing,
And I ran like this all on my way to school.

I Went to School One Morning

How to use this song

Learning objectives

Stepping Stone
Show increasing independence in selecting and carrying out activities.

Early Learning Goal
Be confident to try new activities, initiate ideas and speak in a familiar group. **(PSED)**

Group size
Any size.

Props
Rucksacks, lunch boxes or bags.
Hats and coats.

Sharing the song

Through singing this song, the children will be encouraged to develop their observation skills and to make connections between what they hear and what they see, and what they should do in response to these things. For example, the school bell ringing suggests that they might be late, so they start running. The song links in very well with several themes, such as 'My day', 'Myself', 'Journeys' and 'Where I live'.

Invite the children to carry their rucksacks, lunch boxes or bags, and, if it is not too warm, to wear their hats and coats as they sing this song.

Use the song as part of an activity session or when the children are going on an outing or visit. It could also link in with stories that describe the children's journeys.

Talk about the different things that we can see when we go out. Discuss the differences between what we might see in the town and the country. What other sounds might the children hear on their way to the group?

Activity ideas

- Encourage the children to contribute their own ideas to extend the song and to introduce other movements. For example, 'I saw a big red bus and I drove like this', 'I saw a hungry duck and I quacked like this', 'I saw a bright green frog and jumped like this', and so on. Choose a child in turn to suggest new lines and actions for the song. Invite them to explain their ideas to the group, only offering help if it is needed. **(PSED)**

- It is important for the children to feel confident in their own surroundings. Part of this confidence will stem from being able to recognise some of the features in the place where they live, and in the world around them. Take every opportunity when you are out on trips to point out things that are around them. Encourage the children to look and listen carefully, and to use their other senses of touch and smell. Talk about the features of their environment that they like and dislike. **(KUW)**

- In preparation for playing the board game provided on the photocopiable sheet, invite the children to stand up, sing the song again and go through the various actions vigorously. Decide together which actions are fast, which are slow, and which involve no movement at all. Discuss the actions that would get the children to the setting quickly, for example, running, galloping and so on, and those that would hold them up, such as hopping and walking backwards. **(PD)**

- Copy the photocopiable sheet on to card to make a board game for pairs of children to play. In order to wind down, invite the children to play the game in pairs, taking it in turns to throw a dice and follow the instructions on the squares where they land. Provide support as necessary. **(PD)**

I Went to School One Morning

Start	move back 1 space		move back 1 space
move on 2 spaces			
		move back 2 spaces	
	move on 1 space		Finish

Twinkle, Twinkle, Little Star

Twinkle, Twinkle, Little Star

Twinkle, twinkle, little star.
(Open hands and wiggle fingers up and down.)

How I wonder what you are.
Up above the world so high,
(Stretch both arms above head.)

Like a diamond in the sky.
Twinkle, twinkle, little star.
(Open hands and wiggle fingers up and down.)

How I wonder what you are.

Tell me how you shine so bright.
Giving out your wondrous light.
(Open hands out wide and flat.)

Up above the world so high,
Like a diamond in the sky.
Tell me how you shine so bright.
Giving out your wondrous light.
(Open hands out wide and flat.)

Twinkle, twinkle, little star.
(Open hands and wiggle fingers up and down.)

How I wonder what you are.
Up above the world so high,
(Stretch both arms above head.)

Like a diamond in the sky.
Twinkle, twinkle, little star.
(Open hands and wiggle fingers up and down.)

How I wonder what you are.

Twinkle, Twinkle, Little Star

How to use this song

Learning objectives

Stepping Stone
Show an awareness of change.

Early Learning Goal
Look closely at similarities, differences, patterns and change. **(KUW)**

Group size
Any size.

Props
Silver star stickers.
Garden cane for each child (to make 'star wands' – see below).

Sharing the song

The aim of this song is to help the children to be aware of similarities, differences and changes that are taking place around them, in particular, the change from a light day to a dark night.

The song links with the themes of 'My day', 'My world' and 'Day and night'. This is a good song to introduce at home time, to help the children to wind down at the end of the day.

Help the children to make star wands by sticking silver stars on to the end of garden canes. Suggest that they wave them gently as they sing the song (make sure that they are careful and do not wave the wands too near people's faces).

Talk about dusk and the appearance of stars in the sky. Can the children see stars every night? Discuss cloudy or rainy nights when cloud covers the stars.

Discuss how the moon is often visible in the sky, together with the stars. Explain to the children how it changes in shape, as the moon goes from a full moon to a crescent moon every month.

Activity ideas

- Encourage the children to tell you about their own experiences of night-time. How do they feel when it is dark outside? When they look at the stars, what do they think about? Encourage them to make up their own rhyme about the stars using this model:
  When it's dark and I'm in bed,
  Lots of thoughts go round my head.
  I feel/ think about... **(CLL)**

- Look together at a poster, a simple atlas or books, such as *The Stars: A New Way to See Them* by Hans Augustus Rey (Houghton Mifflin), or *Wishing on a Star* by Fran Lee (Gibbs M Smith Inc.), which show the stars in the sky. Show the children some of the easier star shapes to identify and discuss how specific shapes can be seen when certain stars are joined together in the correct order. Encourage the children to practise number order using the photocopiable sheet. Hand out a copy to each child and ask them to join the stars, starting at number 1 and progressing through to number 10, to form a picture. Use the number line provided if necessary. **(MD)**

- Tell the children some simple information and facts about stars, such as stars appear so small in the sky because they are a very long way away, much further than any of us can imagine; they are very hot and give out a bright light, like the sun; the sun is the closest star to us and therefore gives out the brightest light; stars give out light, in the same way as the sun, but because they are much further away, their light is not as bright; during the day, light is provided by the sun, whereas at night, some light is provided by the stars and the moon. Encourage the children to look out for stars when it gets dark, but remind them never to look directly at the sun. **(KUW)**

Twinkle, Twinkle, Little Star

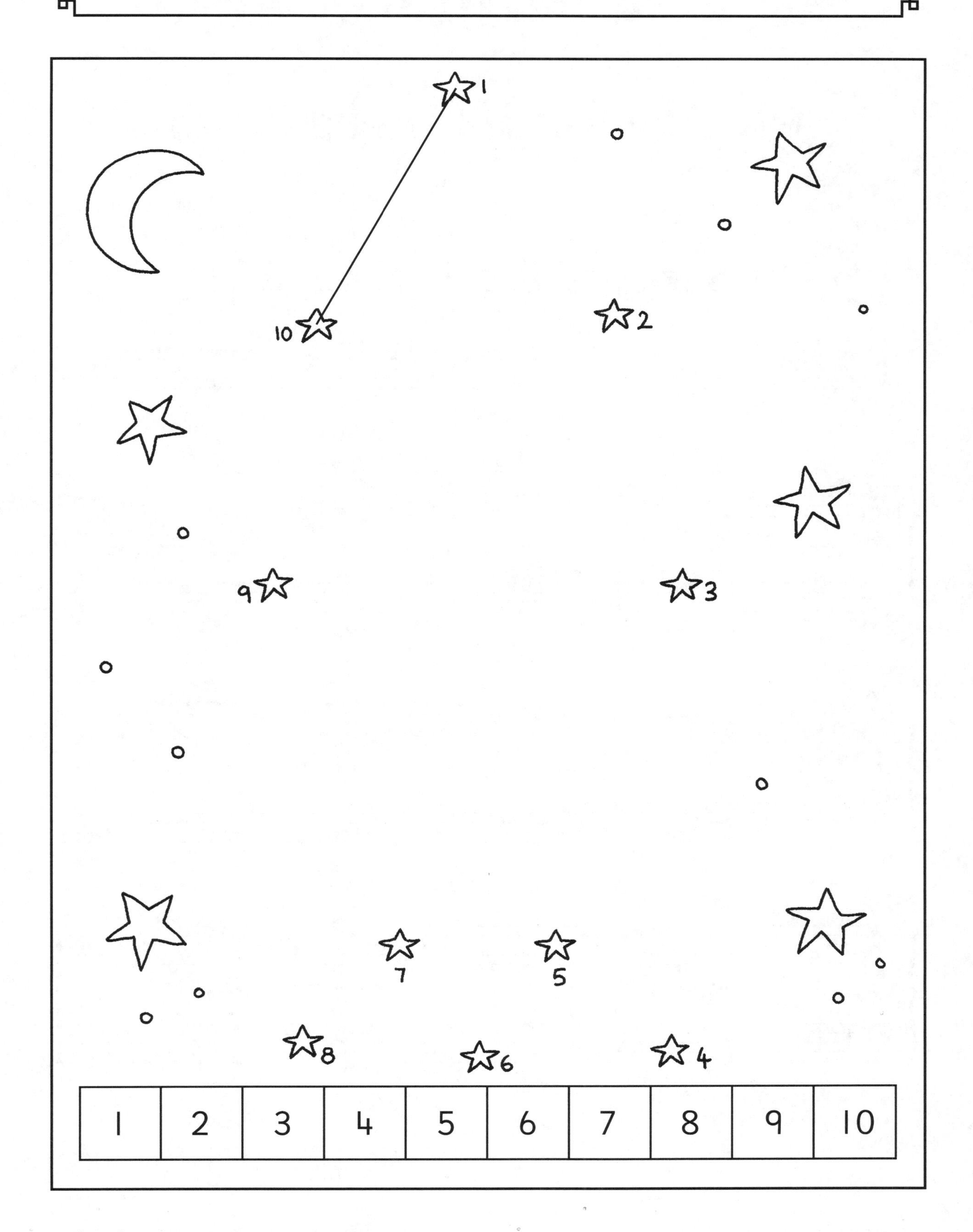

1	2	3	4	5	6	7	8	9	10

Animals

Old MacDonald Had a Farm

Old MacDonald Had a Farm

Old MacDonald had a farm, e-i-e-i-o.
(Walk slowly pretending to carry two heavy buckets.)

And on this farm he had some chicks, e-i-e-i-o.
(Stretch up and pretend to flap wings.)

With a chirp, chirp and a chirp, chirp,
Here a chirp, there a chirp, everywhere a chirp, chirp.
Old MacDonald had a farm, e-i-e-i-o.

Verse 2 – ...And on this farm he had some ducks, e-i-e-i-o.
(Waddle along.)

With a quack, quack and a quack, quack,
Here a quack, there a quack, everywhere a quack, quack. *(and so on)*

Verse 3 – ...And on this farm he had some pigs, e-i-e-i-o.
(Kneel down and pretend to search around in the ground.)

With an oink, oink and an oink, oink,
Here an oink, there an oink, everywhere an oink, oink. *(and so on)*

Verse 4 – ...And on this farm he had some cows, e-i-e-i-o.
(Pretend to be chewing the cud.)

With a moo, moo and a moo, moo,
Here a moo, there a moo, everywhere a moo, moo. *(and so on)*

Verse 5 - ...And on this farm he had two geese, e-i-e-i-o.
(Stretch out neck and look aggressive, while making a hissing noise.)

With a gobble, gobble and a gobble, gobble,
Here a gobble, there a gobble, everywhere a gobble, gobble. *(and so on)*

Verse 6 – ...And on this farm he had some sheep, e-i-e-i-o.
(Run and skip along.)

With a baa, baa here and a baa, baa there,
Here a baa, there a baa, everywhere a baa, baa. *(and so on)*

Old MacDonald Had a Farm

How to use this song

Learning objectives

Stepping Stone
Join in favourite songs.

Early Learning Goal
Sing simple songs from memory, recognise repeated sounds and sound patterns and match movements to music. **(CD)**

Group size
Any size.

Props
Wellington boots.
Two buckets.

Sharing the song

By joining in this song, the children will become aware of the different animals that live on farms and of the variety of noises that those animals make. The song is very suitable for use with the themes of 'Animals' or 'Living things'. Use the song before a group visit to a farm or to link in with stories set on farms.

To introduce the song and to help the children to engage with it, ask who has been on a farm, who the farm belonged to and what they saw there. Talk about the various people who work on farms and the different kinds of animals that live there.

Invite one child to be Old MacDonald and to put on the Wellington boots, and carry two buckets as he or she goes to feed the various animals on the farm.

As the children become more and more involved in the song, encourage them to make suggestions for other animals that might be on the farm and the noises that they would make, to gain confidence to speak up in a group.

Activity ideas

- As part of circle time or when the children are involved in a show-and-tell session, adapt the song as follows. Instead of 'Old MacDonald', substitute the child's name and instead of 'farm', substitute 'house'. Then sing, 'In that house, he had a...' (whatever the show-and-tell item is). Encourage the children to come up with ideas for the rest of the song, for example, 'With a... here, and a... there' and so on. **(CLL)**

- Divide the children into random groups to represent different animals on the farm. Provide a 'field' for each group by roping off different areas of your setting. When your 'animals' are safely in their own 'fields', count how many of each you have. Then ask the children different mathematical problems, for example, 'If one pig escapes, how many do we have now?', 'If two sheep run into the field from the next-door farm, how many sheep will there be now?' and so on. Reinforce this activity by giving each child a copy of the photocopiable sheet and asking them to work out the animal sums. **(MD)**

- Talk about feathers, animal hair, wool, webbed feet, hooves and so on. Examine pictures of animals carefully, encouraging the children to make comparisons. **(CD)**

Old MacDonald Had a Farm

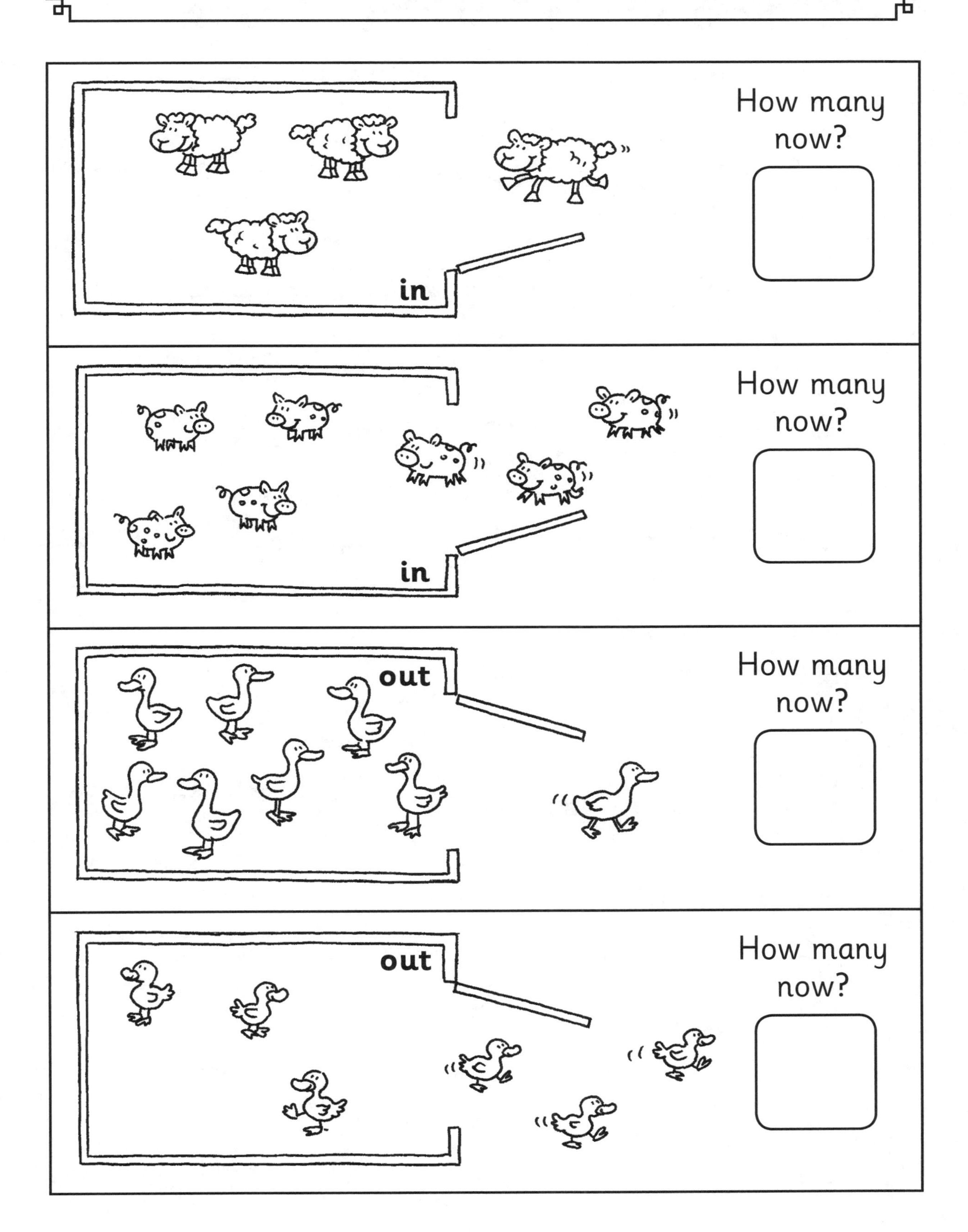

Five Little Speckled Frogs

Five Little Speckled Frogs

(Five children sit in a row, on a bench.)

Five little speckled frogs,
Sat on a speckled log,
Eating some most delicious grubs, 'yum, yum'.
(Pretend to be eating and make appreciative eating noises.)

One jumped into the pool,
(One child gets up and leaps on to the ground in front of them.)

Where it was nice and cool,
Then there were four green speckled frogs.
Glub, glub!
(Puff out cheeks.)

Verse 2 – Four little speckled frogs... *(and so on)*
...Then there were three green speckled frogs.

Verse 3 – Three little speckled frogs... *(and so on)*
...Then there were two green speckled frogs.

Verse 4 – Two little speckled frogs... *(and so on)*
...Then there was one green speckled frog.

Verse 5 – One little speckled frog,
Sat on a speckled log,
Eating some most delicious grubs, 'yum, yum'.
He jumped into the pool,
Where it was nice and cool,
Then there were no more speckled frogs.
Glub, glub!

Five Little Speckled Frogs

How to use this song

Learning objectives

Stepping Stone
Separate a group of three or four objects in different ways, beginning to recognise that the total is still the same.

Early Learning Goal
In practical activities and discussion begin to use the vocabulary involved in adding and subtracting. **(MD)**

Group size
Five children.

Props
Frog masks (see below).

Sharing the song

This song provides a wonderful opportunity to introduce the concept of subtraction and the mathematical words 'less' and 'more'. The children will be able to see that the number of frogs on the bench gets less as more and more frogs jump off. This song links in with the themes of 'Animals', 'Life cycles' and 'Living things'.

Use the photocopiable sheet to make frog masks (see PD Activity ideas, right) and suggest that the children wear their frog masks as they sing the song.

Use this song as a game to reinforce learning when the children are working with numbers and to help teach the important concept of 'less' and 'more', which underpins much mathematical learning. Talk about everyday situations that involve this kind of mathematical understanding, for example, if friends come to tea, will we need more food or less? If I use two stamps to stick on to these letters, will I have more or less stamps left in my book?

Activity ideas

- Provide the children with two piles of five building blocks. Encourage them to experiment by moving a brick at a time from one pile to the other. Point out that as they subtract from one pile, this pile contains less bricks. As they add to the other pile, this contains correspondingly more bricks. Eventually, there will be none left in the first pile, as they have all been removed to the second pile. Link this to what happens in the song. **(MD)**

- Discuss the life cycle of the frog as the frogspawn (eggs in jelly) hatch into tadpoles with tails, which eventually grow legs and develop into tiny frogs. The tiny frogs grow into big frogs, which lay eggs and the cycle begins again. Make several visits to ponds during the spring and early summer to see the progress of frogspawn becoming frogs. Alternatively, visit an organised nature reserve, such as the RSPB reserves or the local Wildlife Trust's reserves, to see examples of frogspawn in captive displays. If it is not possible to see either frogspawn or tadpoles, show the children pictures in books or on the Internet. **(KUW)**

- Invite the children to colour in the frog mask and tongue templates on the photocopiable sheet. Ask them to think carefully about the colours that would be appropriate to use, by showing them plenty of examples from books. Discuss the meaning of 'speckled' and make sure that their frogs are. Help them to cut out the masks and tongues carefully. Encourage the children to come up with as many ideas as possible for attaching the tongues to the masks. Which would be most effective? Attach elastic or string to the masks so that the children can wear them while singing the song and performing the actions. **(PD)**

Five Little Speckled Frogs

There's a Worm Who's Wriggling in the Jungle

There's a Worm Who's Wriggling in the Jungle

(Wiggle hand and arm.)
There's a worm who's wriggling in the jungle,
And his name is wiggly woo.
There's a worm who's wriggling in the jungle,
And all that he can do.
Is wriggle all day and wriggle all night.
You might say he's a terrible fright.
There's a worm who's wriggling in the jungle,
And his name is wiggly woo.

There's a worm who's wriggling in the jungle,
And his name is wiggly woo.
There's a worm who's wriggling in the jungle,
And all that he can do.
Is wriggle along and wriggle around.
(Move wiggling hand and arm across in front of your body and around in a circle.)

And wriggle himself back under the ground.
(Move wiggling hand and arm vertically downwards.)

There's a worm who's wriggling in the jungle,
And his name is wiggly woo.

(Wiggle hand and arm.)
There's a worm who's wriggling in the jungle,
And his name is wiggly woo.
There's a worm who's wriggling in the jungle,
And all that he can do.
Is wriggle all day and wriggle all night.
You might say he's a terrible fright.
There's a worm who's wriggling in the jungle,
And his name is wiggly woo.

There's a Worm Who's Wriggling in the Jungle

How to use this song

Learning objectives

Stepping Stone
Manage body to create intended movements.

Early Learning Goal
Travel around, under, over and through balancing and climbing equipment. **(PD)**

Group size
Any size.

Props
Children's long socks in plain, muted colours.

Sharing the song

The children will enjoy trying to move their bodies like worms, twisting around, under, over, up and down, and through, imagining that they are breaking up the soil and avoiding barriers, such as stones and roots in the soil. The purpose of practising these movements is to increase their control over their bodies. The song links in well with the themes of 'Animals', 'Minibeasts' and 'Living things'.

Ask the children to put a sock on their hand and pull it up round their arm, so that it looks like a worm as they sing this song.

Use this song when the children are out in the garden, during discussion about minibeasts or when they are playing on outside play equipment. Discuss how hard earth is broken up by worms as they wriggle down into the soil and appear back at the surface again. Explain that although it does not appear that they are doing a useful job, they really are. Explain that without worms, it would be much more difficult for plants to grow successfully.

Activity ideas

- Make copies of the photocopiable sheet and invite the children to practise their pencil control by following the dotted line between, over, under and around the objects in the obstacle course. Make sure that they hold their pencils correctly, near the point, with a tight grip between the thumb and first and second fingers, and tell them to take their time to cover the dotted line as accurately as possible. **(CLL)**

- Help the children to set up a wormery, so that they can see what happens when worms burrow down through the soil. In a narrow glass tank, put a layer of sand, a layer of earth and then a layer of damp leaves. Repeat these layers once or twice more. Introduce several large worms into the top of the tank and cover the whole thing with a black sugar-paper 'hat'. Water lightly. After a week or so, remove the cover. Several burrows should be visible in the layers and a certain amount of mixing of the layers should have occurred. The worms may be visible at first, but will quickly disappear in the light. Replace the cover and examine again after another week. **(KUW)**

- Set up an obstacle course and provide benches to climb along and over, hoops to climb through, cones to manoeuvre around and go between, equipment to climb under, and ramps to go up and down. Encourage the children to follow the course, practising the movements and increasing the speed in which they can complete the course. **(PD)**

There's a Worm Who's Wriggling in the Jungle

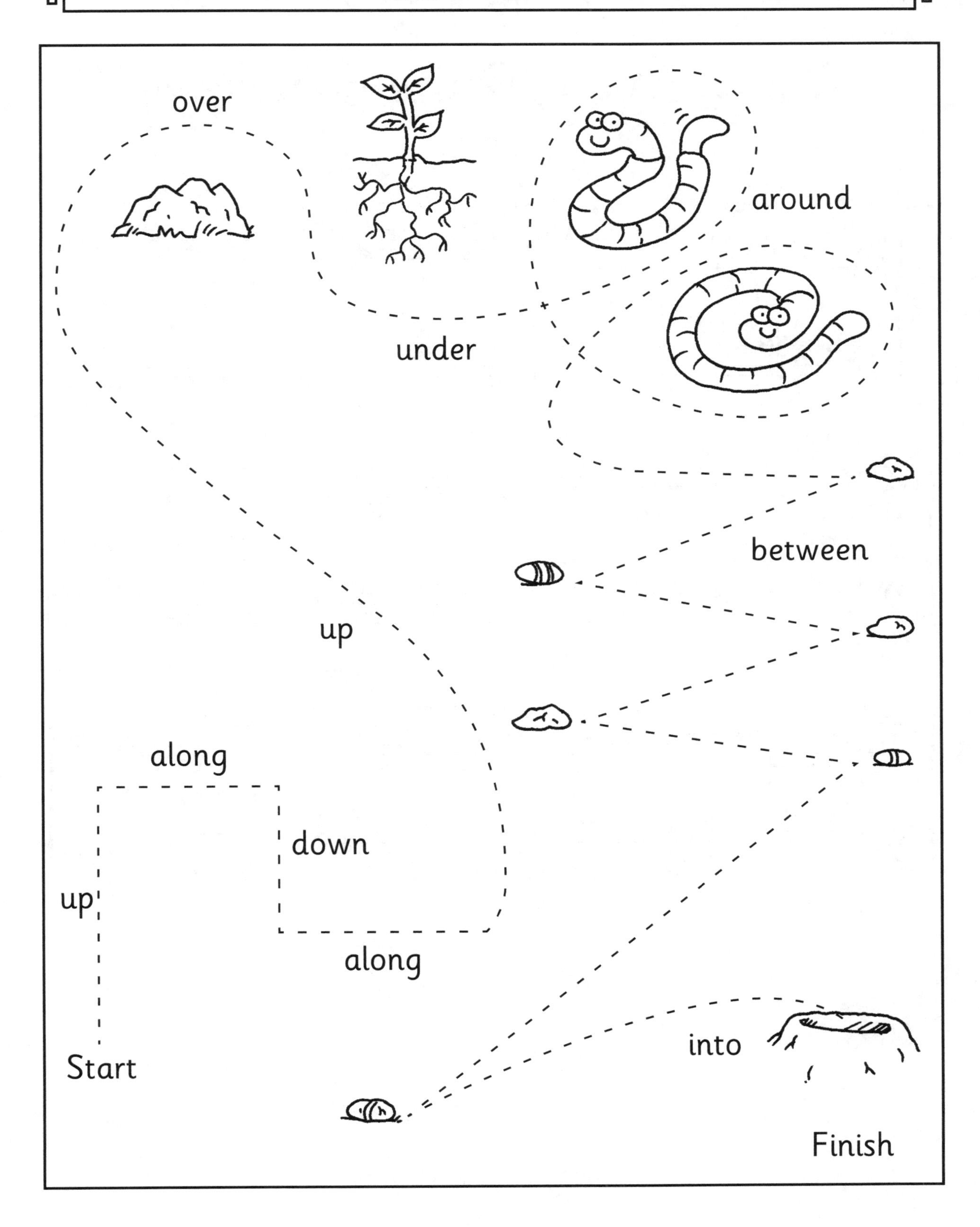

Growing

Mary, Mary, Quite Contrary

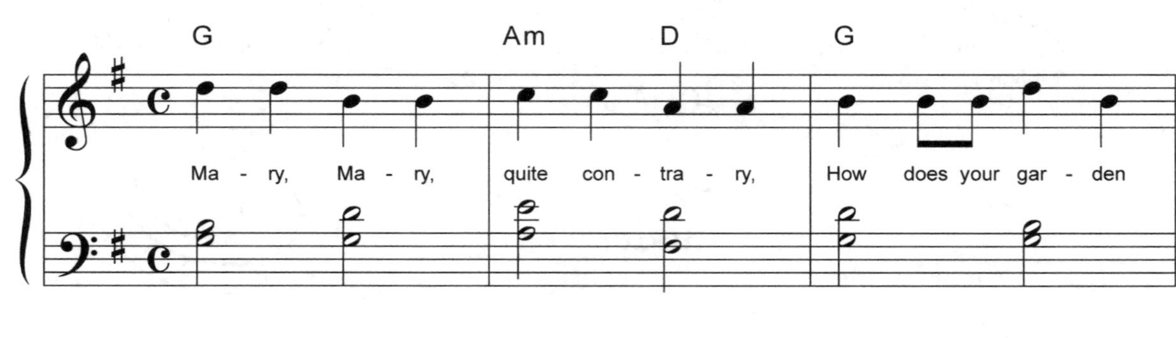

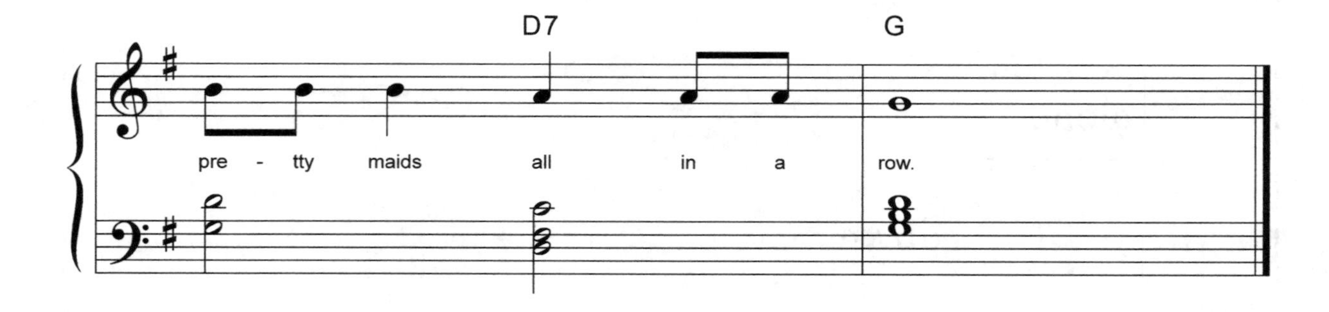

Mary, Mary, Quite Contrary

Mary, Mary, quite contrary,
How does your garden grow?
With silver bells and cockle shells,
And pretty maids all in a row.
(Girls in the group stand in a row, smiling sweetly, and take turns to curtsey.)

(Repeat twice)

Silver bells and cockle shells,
And pretty maids all in a row.
(Girls in the group stand in a row, smiling sweetly, and take turns to curtsey.)

Silver bells and cockle shells,
And pretty maids all in a row.
(Girls in the group stand in a row, smiling sweetly, and take turns to curtsey.)

Mary, Mary, Quite Contrary

How to use this song

Learning objectives

Stepping Stone
Use one object to represent another, even when the objects have few characteristics in common.

Early Learning Goal
Use their imagination in art and design. **(CD)**

Group size
Any size.

Props
String of small silver bells.
Cockle shells.

Sharing the song

This song fits in with the theme of 'Growing'. It is a gentle song, to be enjoyed during a quiet spell in the children's day, or perhaps at home time.

Talk to the children about pretty gardens and what kind of things usually grow in them. Mention grass, trees, shrubs and flowers. Why is Mary's garden not an ordinary garden?

Ask two children to hold up the string of silver bells and the rest of the group to hold up cockle shells, as they sing the song, which will encourage the children to be creative and imaginative. Ask them to think of different ways of designing and decorating an area to make it look attractive, which will help them to be aware of colour, texture, shape and form.

Activity ideas

- Discuss the meaning of 'contrary' and why Mary is being deliberately different when she chooses to have bells, shells and maids in her garden, rather than flowers. Have any of the children been accused of being contrary when they have been very obstinate and insisted on doing something out of the ordinary? Do the children think that Mary should be encouraged to have whatever she wants to have in her garden? **(PSED)**

- Discuss what real plants and flowers need to help them to grow properly. Talk about good earth, lots of sunshine and plenty of rain. Without any of these components, plants will shrivel up and die. Invite the children to tell you what might be needed to keep Mary's garden in good condition. Talk about silver polish to keep the bells shiny, soapy water to wash the shells, and hairbrushes and paint to keep the wooden maids looking smart. **(KUW)**

- Give each child a shallow tray with wet sand in the bottom. Encourage them to design a non-conventional garden in the tray using a wide variety of collage materials, such as bottle tops, wool, straws, buttons, silver foil, paper clips and so on. Ask the children to observe real gardens carefully and to be as creative as possible when they reproduce gardens with different materials. Emphasise the differences between real and non-conventional gardens by asking the children to find the ten real flowers hidden in Mary's garden on the photocopiable sheet. **(CD)**

Mary, Mary, Quite Contrary

One Potato, Two Potato

One Potato, Two Potato

(Children sit in pairs, facing each other.)

In my little garden,
Now promise you won't laugh,
I haven't any flowers,
(Open hands flat and shake head.)

And I haven't any grass.
But now I'm going to dig and plant,
(Pretend to dig by cupping hand and making a shovelling movement close to the floor. Put 'potatoes' carefully into imaginary holes in the floor, smooth the earth over and gently pat the floor.)

And soon I'll have a show.
With a bit of sun,
(Make a circle with your hands.)

And a bit of rain,
(Open hands and flutter fingers.)

There'll be a lovely row.
(Point along a row with the forefinger.)

(Repeat)

One potato, two potato, three potato, four.
(Make both hands into fists to build a 'tower' on the floor, with the first child putting one fist down, the second child putting his first fist on top, the first child putting his second fist on top of that, and second child putting his second fist on top of that.)

Five potato, six potato, seven potato, more.
One potato, two potato, three potato, four.
Five potato, six potato, seven potato, more.
(Continue counting to eight, removing the fist from the bottom of the pile and placing it on to the top of the pile, so that the 'tower' gets higher and higher.)

(Repeat whole song three times)

One Potato, Two Potato

How to use this song

Learning objectives

Stepping Stone
Show an interest in numbers and counting.

Early Learning Goal
Say and use number names in order in familiar contexts. **(MD)**

Group size
Any size.

Props
Small fork and trowel.
Wellington boots.
Small basket full of potatoes.
Percussion instruments.

Sharing the song

The object of this song is to encourage the children to count accurately and in the correct order, introducing the concept of 'more' as the numbers get bigger. The song is especially relevant to the themes of 'Growing', 'Food' or 'Seasons'.

While singing this song, invite one child to put on the wellington boots and dig the 'ground' with a fork and trowel, while a second child 'plants' the potatoes and a third pretends to cover them up with soil. Encourage the rest of the group to perform the song's actions from page 47.

Invite all of the children to join in with the chorus of this song and use it as part of a circle-time activity when the group can accompany their singing with different percussion instruments. Introduce the song by asking the children if they know where potatoes come from. Do any of their parents grow potatoes or other vegetables in their gardens or on an allotment?

Activity ideas

- Ask the children what they would expect to see in a garden and discuss how the garden in the song is different from those described by the children. Why is the owner of this garden worried that people might laugh? Gently explain how sometimes people think that things that are different are not as good. Why is this wrong? Explain why it is important to understand everyone's needs, views, feelings and ideas, and to respect, accept and be sensitive to them. **(PSED)**

- Play some Scottish dancing music or other dance music with a definite beat to the count of eight. Encourage the children to clap in time with the music, at the same time as repeatedly counting to eight out loud. **(MD)**

- Show the children some seed potatoes. Let them examine them and point out how the roots come out from the potato. Invite the children to plant two potatoes in compost in two large flower pots. Keep one of these pots dry and in the dark, while watering the other and keeping it in bright light. Notice how leaves will begin to grow on one and not the other. Discuss why this is. Explain that the potatoes grow on roots underground while the leaves of the potato plant grow above ground. Hand out copies of the photocopiable sheet and ask the children to draw potato plants with the leaves above the ground and the potatoes below the line. Invite different children to draw given numbers of potatoes and to write in the number of potatoes on their sheet, so that the drawings can be collated and used as a number line. **(KUW)**

One Potato, Two Potato

Tranport

The Wheels on the Bus

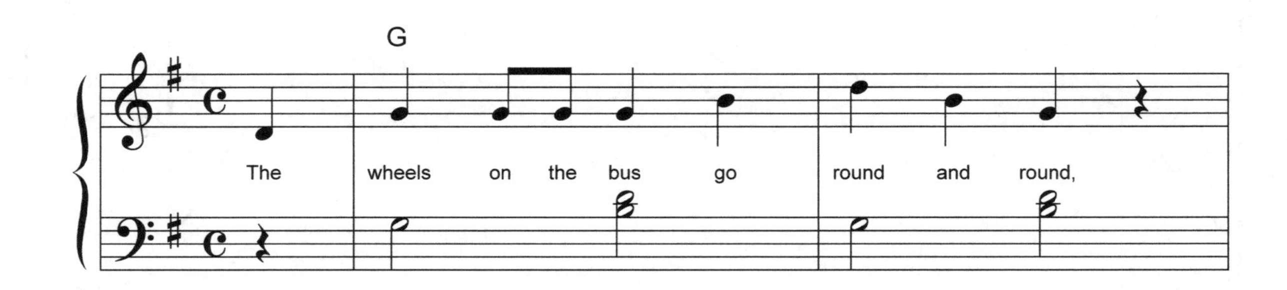

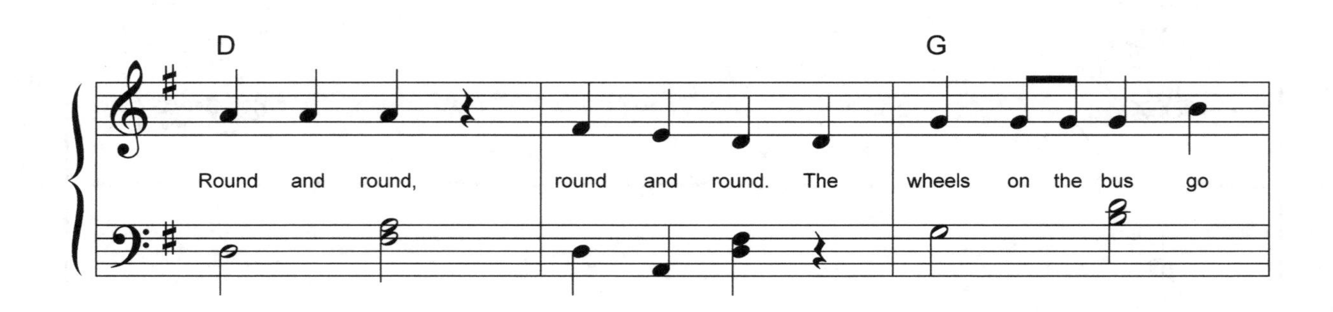

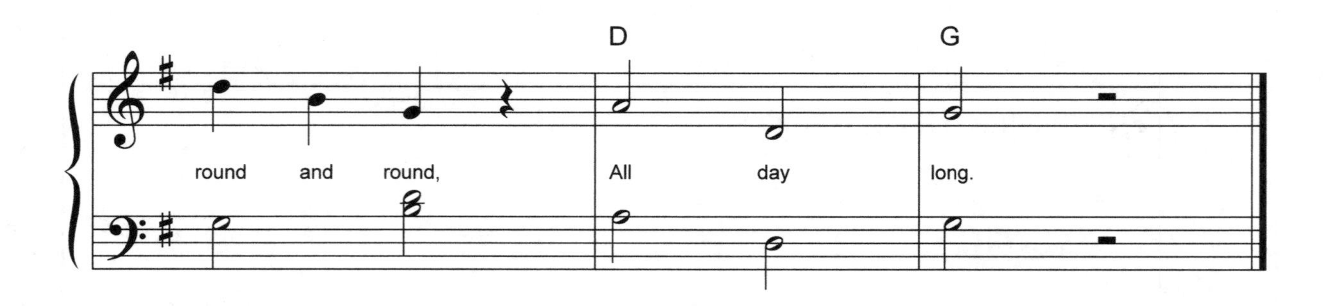

The Wheels on the Bus

(Sit on the floor.)

The wheels on the bus go round and round,
(Move both hands round in a big circle.)

Round and round, round and round.
The wheels on the bus go round and round,
All day long.

The horn on the bus goes beep, beep, beep,
(Close the four fingers of the hand against the thumb, to indicate squeezing the bulb of a horn.)

Beep, beep, beep, beep, beep, beep.
The horn on the bus goes beep, beep, beep,
All day long.

The people on the bus bounce up and down,
(Gently bounce up and down on the floor.)

Up and down, up and down.
The people on the bus bounce up and down,
All day long.

The wipers on the bus go swish, swish, swish,
(Rest elbow on the floor in front of them, moving their whole forearm from side to side.)

Swish, swish, swish, swish, swish, swish.
The wipers on the bus go swish, swish, swish,
All day long.

The bell on the bus goes ting-a-ling-a-ling,
(Press an imaginary bell with the point of their index finger.)

Ting-a-ling-a-ling, ting-a-ling-a-ling.
The bell on the bus goes ting-a-ling-a-ling,
All day long.

The conductor on the bus says, 'Tickets please!',
(Shout out 'Tickets please!'.)

'Tickets please!', 'Tickets please'.
The conductor on the bus says, 'Tickets please!',
All day long.

The Wheels on the Bus

How to use this song

Learning objectives

Stepping Stone
Show an interest in what they see and hear.

Early Learning Goal
Respond in a variety of ways to what they see and hear. **(CD)**

Group size
Any size.

Props
Bus conductor's hat.
Shoulder bag with loose change.
Bus tickets.

Sharing the song

The aim of this song is to encourage the children to look and listen very carefully so that they are fully aware of what is going on around them. The song can be used with the themes of 'Transport', 'Journeys' or 'People who help us'.

Choose one child to be the bus conductor and invite them to put on the conductor's hat and carry the shoulder bag. Encourage this child to move around the group and give out tickets and change.

Sing this song when the children have recently arrived at the group, as some may have had a bus journey. Point out that buses can be different colours, but all have very large wheels, horns to warn other traffic that they are there, wipers to clear rain off the windscreen, and bells for the passengers to push so that they can stop the bus at the bus stop. Explain that some buses have conductors, although in many new buses, the driver collects the money and issues tickets as well as driving.

Activity ideas

- Explain that as a lot of different people travel on buses at certain times of the day, they can get very busy. Discuss how we need to respect the needs of everyone else on the bus. Ask the children what should be done in the following circumstances: a lady gets on the bus carrying a small child and there is no seat for her; you are trying to get on a bus when lots of people are trying to get off; you need to get past lots of people in order to reach the door to get off the bus, and so on. Set up a bus role-play to practise what they have learned. **(PSED)**

- Talk about the importance of being polite. Instead of demanding something, it is polite to use the word 'please', and when we are given what we want, it is polite to say, 'thank you'. Tell the children to notice, in the song, how the conductor says, 'Tickets please!'. Arrange the children in pairs and invite them to ask one another, politely, for something in the room. When they are given what they want, make sure that they respond correctly by saying 'thank you'. **(CLL)**

- Show the children pictures of various forms of transport. Notice how all of them have wheels, but these vary considerably in size. Look carefully at some of the different wheels. Point out spokes, hub caps, tyres with different patterns on them, and narrow and wide tyres. Give out copies of the photocopiable sheet and encourage the children to match up the various wheels to the different forms of transport. Invite the children to make pictures of wheels and tyre patterns. Use cotton reels, potato mashers and different-sized rings and hoops to make wheel patterns, and use a selection of rubber tyres (from toy cars, bicycles and cars) to make the tyre prints. Both should be dipped into fairly runny poster paint. **(CD)**

The Wheels on the Bus

I'm a Steam Train a-Rolling

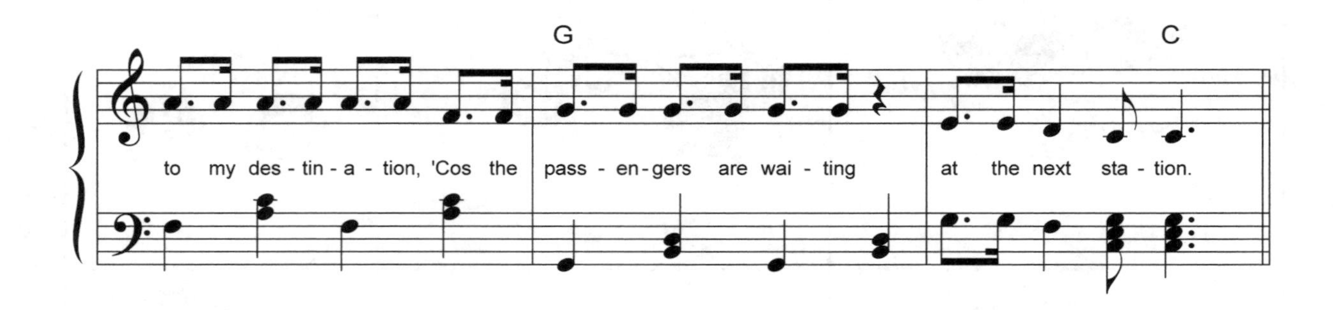

I'm a Steam Train a-Rolling

(Children can pretend to be steam trains, running with little steps and moving both bent arms from the shoulders, in a circular movement, to represent the wheels.)

I'm a steam train a-rolling down the track,
Over the rails I go clickety clack.
Hurry, hurry, hurry to my destination,
'Cos the passengers are waiting at the next station.

The fireman's on the foot plate,
Putting coal on the fire.
(Lift up imaginary lumps of coal and throw them on the fire.)

The steam pressure's rising higher and higher.
Chuff! Chuff! Chuff! Will I make it up that hill?
(Slow down to a walk and puff and pant.)

'Woow, woow' goes my whistle, yes of course I will.

I'm a steam train a-rolling down the track,
Over the rails I go clickety clack.
Hurry, hurry, hurry to my destination,
'Cos the passengers are waiting at the next station.

I'm a Steam Train a-Rolling

How to use this song

Learning objectives

Stepping Stone
Extend vocabulary, especially by grouping and naming.

Early Learning Goal
Extend their vocabulary, exploring the meanings and sounds of new words. **(CLL)**

Group size
Any size.

Props
Fireperson's cap.
Small shovel and box of 'coal', made from black sugar paper.

Sharing the song

One of the aims of this song is to introduce the children to new words associated with the familiar subject of trains. The song will also help the children to listen out for different phonic sounds in words, particularly the blended sounds at the beginning of words. The song links in with the themes of 'Transport' and 'Journeys'.

Let one child be the fireperson and wear the cap. Make some 'coal' by scrunching up strips of black sugar paper. Invite the fireperson to shovel 'coal' on to a 'fire' to speed the train along.

Sing this song when you are reading the children a story, such as the *Thomas the Tank Engine* series (Egmont Books) or other stories about trains. It could also be used as part of a physical play activity.

Many of the children will have never seen a steam train. Encourage those that have seen a steam train to share their knowledge with the others. Tell the children that modern trains are powered either by diesel or by electricity, whereas a steam train needs to burn coal to drive it along.

Activity ideas

- Remind the children of the individual sounds of the letters of the alphabet. Explain that as well as these individual sounds, two letter sounds can run together (a blend) to make a new sound, for example, 'tr', 'st', 'cl', 'pl' and 'pr'. Encourage the children to chase the individual sounds together in order to get the new sound. Reinforce this learning by giving the children copies of the photocopiable sheet and asking them to match the pictures to the initial sounds, by drawing a line from the picture to the blends provided at the top of the page. **(CLL)**

- Explain how a steam train is driven along by a coal fire. The fire heats water to produce steam and when there is lots of steam (like a kettle boiling), the train has enough power to go very fast and climb steep hills. Sing through the rhyme slowly, stopping to explain some of the words that the children may not have met before or may not know the meaning of, for example, 'destination' – where the train is going to; 'passengers' – people travelling on the train; 'foot-plate' – a little platform on the train where the fireperson stands; 'fireperson' – the person in charge of keeping the fire on the train going; 'coal' – lumps of black stones used to light fires and produce heat. **(KUW)**

- Practise the song actions in fast and slow motion, indicating a train going down a hill and climbing up one, speeding up and slowing down between the two types of action. Encourage the children to move with care and control, taking care not to bump into anyone else in the confined space around them. **(PD)**

I'm a Steam Train

tr	cl	st	pl

__ __

__ __

__ __

__ __

__ __

__ __

__ __

__ __

People who help us

Cobbler, Cobbler, Mend My Shoe

Cobbler, Cobbler, Mend My Shoe

Cobbler, cobbler mend my shoe.
(Pretend to hammer shoe.)

Get it done by half-past two.
Half-past two is much too late,
(Point at wrist where watch might be and shake head.)

Get it done by half-past eight.

Cobbler, cobbler mend my shoe.
(Pretend to hammer shoe.)

Get it done by half-past two.
Half-past two is much too late,
(Point at wrist where watch might be and shake head.)

Get it done by half-past eight.

Cobbler, cobbler mend my shoe.
(Pretend to hammer shoe.)

Get it done by half-past two.
Half-past two is much too late,
(Point at wrist where watch might be and shake head.)

Get it done by half-past eight.

Cobbler, cobbler mend my shoe.
(Pretend to hammer shoe.)

Get it done by half-past two.
Half-past two is much too late,
(Point at wrist where watch might be and shake head.)

Get it done by half-past eight.

Cobbler, Cobbler, Mend My Shoe

How to use this song

Learning objectives

Stepping Stone
Initiate conversation, attend to and take account of what others say, and use talk to resolve disagreements.

Early Learning Goal
Interact with others, negotiating plans and activities and taking turns in conversation. **(CLL)**

Group size
Any size.

Props
Apron.
Toy hammer.
Pairs of shoes.

Sharing the song

The aim of this song is to encourage the children to interact with one another, learning to listen as well as to speak and engage in true conversation. They will also learn how to negotiate and resolve disagreements through talk. This song links in with the themes of 'Occupations' and 'People who help us'. This would be a good song to use with *The Elves and the Shoemaker*, *Favourite Tales* series (Ladybird Books).

Suggest that one child puts on the apron, holds a shoe and pretends to mend it by hammering on the sole.

Discuss why shoes need to be mended. Explain that the soles eventually get holes in them because they get worn down by hard surfaces. The heels get worn down because they are bearing the weight of our bodies. Talk about the different materials that shoes are made from, for example, leather, plastic, fabric and rubber.

Activity ideas

- In the rhyme, do the children think that the customer is being polite to the shoe-mender? Do they say 'please' or 'thank you'? Are they thinking of the shoe-mender or themselves when they demand that the job is done by 'half-past eight'? Have they thought about how long it might take to do? Help the children to appreciate the work involved by asking them to complete the photocopiable sheet, by cutting out the shoe-mending pictures and sticking them on to a piece of paper in the correct order. **(PSED)**

- Set up role-play situations in the home corner and invite two children at a time into the area. Give them a hypothetical situation such as, 'Go the shop and buy something for tea', or, 'Visit the doctor because you are not well'. Encourage the children to tell their partner what they want and to ask for their partner's advice. For example, 'Can you tell me what food you would recommend today?' and, 'What should I do to make myself feel better?'. Only offer help as required, leaving the children to negotiate with each other as much as they can. **(CLL)**

- Look at the soles of the children's shoes. Divide them into groups with smooth leather soles and another with ridged rubber ones. In turn, invite the children from the two groups to walk up a small slide. Ask them who is less likely to slip on the slope. Let them test this out. Were their predictions correct? **(KUW)**

Cobbler, Cobbler Mend My Shoe

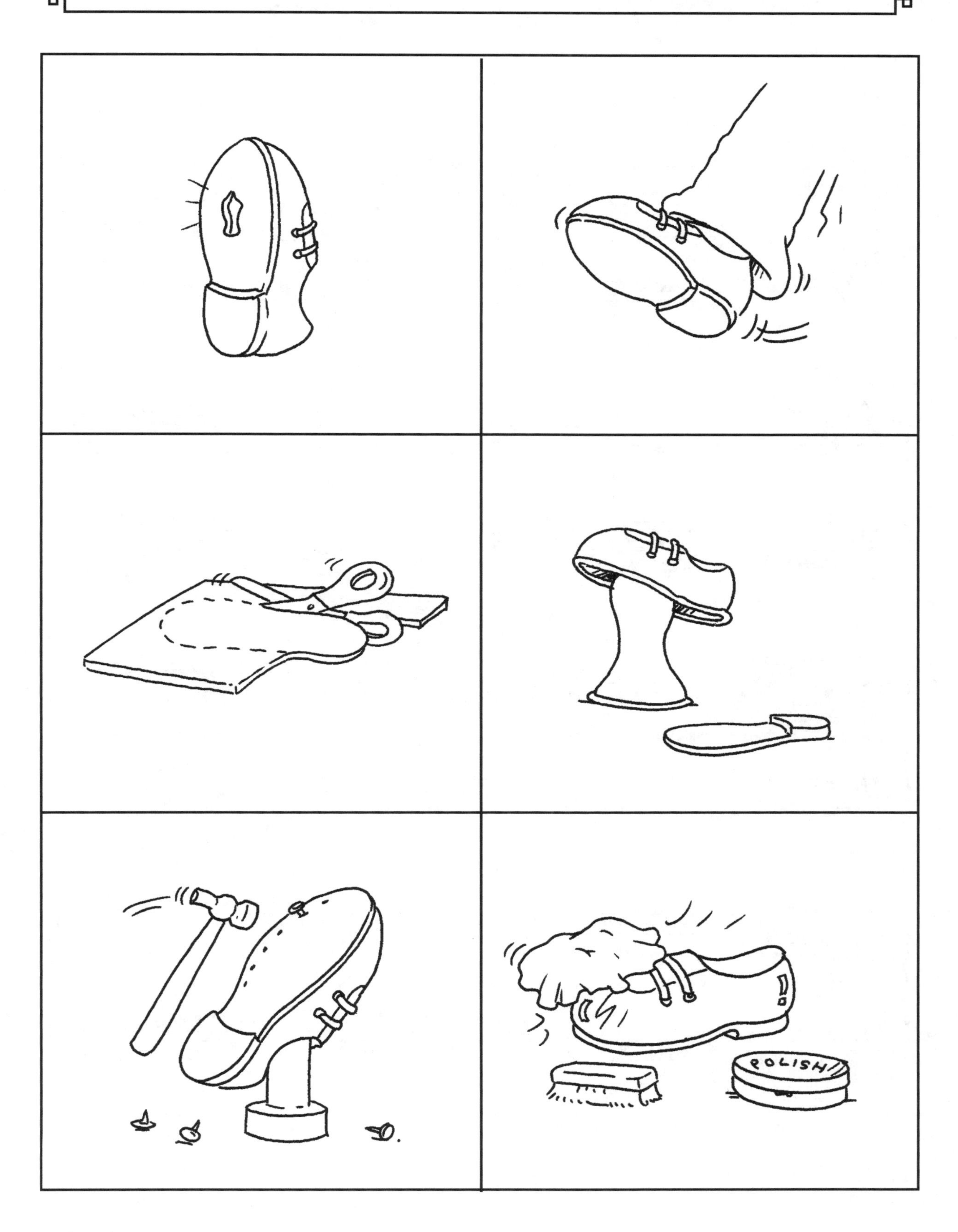

London Bridge is Falling Down

London Bridge is Falling Down

(Sit on floor, legs outstretched.)

London Bridge is falling down,
(Flop forward from their sitting position.)

Falling down, falling down.
London Bridge is falling down,
My fair lady.

(Repeat twice)

We'll build it up with wood and clay,
(Build fists up, one on top of the other.)

Wood and clay, wood and clay.
Build it up with wood and clay,
My fair lady.

Wood and clay will wash away,
(Move flat palms from side to side.)

Wash away, wash away.
Wood and clay will wash away,
My fair lady.

Build it up with iron and steel,
Iron and steel, iron and steel.
Build it up with iron and steel,
My fair lady.

Iron and steel will bend and bow,
(Bow heads forwards.)

Bend and bow, bend and bow.
Iron and steel will bend and bow,
My fair lady.

London Bridge is falling down,
(Flop forward from their sitting position.)

Falling down, falling down.
London Bridge is falling down,
My fair lady.

Build it up with silver and gold,
Silver and gold, silver and gold.
Build it up with silver and gold,
My fair lady.

Silver and gold will be stole away,
(Grab the air in front of them.)

Stole away, stole away.
Silver and gold will be stole away,
My fair lady.

Set a man to watch all night,
(Hold hands like binoculars in front of their eyes.)

Watch all night, watch all night.
Set a man to watch all night
My fair lady.

London Bridge is Falling Down

How to use this song

Learning objectives

Stepping Stone
Demonstrate increasing skill and control in the use of blocks and construction sets.

Early Learning Goal
Handle tools, objects, construction and malleable materials safely and with increasing control. **(PD)**

Group size
Any size.

Props
Dungarees.
Toy tools.
Yellow builder's helmet.

Sharing the song

The aim of this song is to encourage the children to increase their manual dexterity and learn how to handle tools effectively. It will also help to develop their ability to use building blocks and construction sets effectively. The song links in with the themes of 'People who help us', 'Materials', 'Building' and 'My world'. Use this song when the children are playing with construction materials or making models.

Choose children to take turns to be builders, wearing the dungarees and helmet, and working with the tools.

Talk about bridges that the children may have seen. These could range from the tiniest bridge across a stream, pedestrian bridges over motorways, suspension bridges over rivers to some of the most famous bridges in the world, such as London Bridge, Sydney Harbour Bridge and the Golden Gate in San Francisco.

Activity ideas

- Look together with the children at simple 2-D shapes and help them to recognise squares, rectangles, circles and triangles. Which shape has three sides? Explain that this shape is often used in bridges because it makes them very strong. Encourage the children to draw a bridge with some triangle shapes helping to hold it up. **(MD)**

- Talk about the various materials mentioned in the song and think about what they are used for. Let the children experiment, in a water tray, with pieces of wood and lumps of clay. Help them to see why wood and clay would 'wash away', and therefore be unsuitable for mending the bridge. Show the children how thick wire or other pliable metal 'bends and bows', and let them try for themselves using paper clips or paper fasteners. Why might silver and gold be stolen? **(KUW)**

- Encourage children to design and make their own bridges out of recyclable materials, or with building blocks and construction kits. Provide plenty of toy transport that can go both under and over the bridge. Explain that small bridges are built to carry people across obstacles, whereas bigger ones have to carry cars, lorries and often trains as well. Explain that the bigger the bridge, the stronger it needs to be. Remind the children that bridges also need to have space for traffic to pass underneath them. **(PD)**